Little Karl

Written by M. Earl Smith

Illustrated by E. A. Santoli

MICHELKIN | PUBLISHING
ROSWELL, NEW MEXICO
BOOKS.MICHELKIN.COM

ISBN: 0-9980672-1-0
ISBN-13: 978-0-9980672-1-6

DEDICATION

M. Earl Smith

To the proletariat.
"...it is essential to educate the educator himself."
Karl Marx

E. A. Santoli

To my family, who have always encouraged me.

Little Karl and his mother were out for a walk one fine Sunday morning.
It was a sunny day, perfect for strolling and taking in the sights of the city!

One of Little Karl's favorite things to do was ask his mother questions.
After all, there was so much to know, and so little that he knew!
His mother always did her best to answer, although, to be fair, Little Karl asked a LOT of
questions.

As they walked, they soon came across a poor man, asleep in the street.
Little Karl looked at his mother, confused. "Why doesn't he go home to sleep?"
His mother shook her head. "Because, Little Karl, he does not have a home. He hasn't worked hard enough for it."

Shouldn't everyone have a home? Little Karl thought.

As they walked on, they came upon a puppy.
The little puppy barked happily and Little Karl petted it and laughed. He could not help but notice how skinny the puppy was.
His mother scolded him. "Little Karl, leave that puppy alone. It's not had enough food, and it's probably sick."

Shouldn't everyone have food? Little Karl thought.

They walked on, and soon came upon a woman with a sign that said: WILL WORK FOR FOOD.
  Little Karl tugged at the hem of his mother's dress. "Why doesn't anyone hire this woman?"
His mother rolled her eyes. "Because she has no skills or schooling. Why should she have a job?"

Shouldn't everyone have work? Little Karl thought.

Little Karl and his mother walked on. Soon, they came across a man, asleep on a bench. He was still in his dirty work uniform.

Little Karl cleared his throat. "Mother, why is that man sleeping on that bench? Is he homeless too?"

Little Karl's mother sighed. "No, Little Karl. I'm sure he has a home. Look at his uniform, sweet child. He has a job! I'm sure it's the type where he has to work very hard."

Should people have to work so hard? Little Karl thought.

Little Karl and his mother rounded a corner. There stood a boy, screaming about loaves of bread for sale. As hard as he tried, Karl's mother did not buy a loaf.

Little Karl stared at the little boy in wonder. "Mother, why are those children working? I don't work!"

Little Karl's mother groaned. "His family is not like ours. He must work so that they can eat."

Why should children have to work? Little Karl thought.

As they walked on, Little Karl noticed a couple in an alley. The girl was well dressed, yet crying. The young man looked at her in agony, his plain clothes showing how poor he was.

Little Karl could not help but stare. "Mother, why are they so upset?"

Little Karl's mother shook her head. "He says he loves her, but he is the son of a farmer and she the daughter of a great count. They can never wed."

Shouldn't people love whomever they want? Little Karl thought.

As they passed the church, one of the solemn-looking priests came out to greet Little Karl's mother. They left Little Karl standing alone for a moment, speaking in quiet tones.
When Little Karl's mother returned, she looked rather upset.
"What's wrong mother?" Little Karl asked.
She waved her hand, dismissing his worry. "Nothing, sweet child. We must always remember that God wants us to pay our tithes."

Why does only the priest know what God wants? Little Karl thought.

Little Karl's mother decided to cheer him up. Stopping in front of a vendor, she waited as another mother bought her little boy a small apple.

When it was Little Karl's turn, his mother got him the biggest apple the vendor had.

Before he could ask, she laughed. "Your father does well, Little Karl, and we have the money to afford bigger apples!

Shouldn't everyone have the same amount of apples? Little Karl thought.

As they rounded the corner for home, Little Karl and his mother saw a rather fat man, dressed in a nice suit.

Little Karl's mother gave him a wide path. In fact, it seemed that she was doing her best to avoid him.

Little Karl remained silent as she whispered. "He is the richest man in town, and he owns the factory. We do not want to upset him."

19

Little Karl was upset.

Why should my mother fear this man, and why is he more important because he owns a factory?

As Little Karl and his mother went inside, his mother spoke in a stern voice. "Little Karl, it's time for your nap."

Little Karl hated his naps! There was no way to ask questions as he napped. He protested, but with no luck.

"Come, Little Karl, and no fuss! If you are a good boy, I shall answer five questions for you!"

Little Karl loved to ask questions! It was not long before he was settled into his bed, eyes wide with excitement.

Little Karl's mother offered a tired smile. "Now, my sweet boy, what are your questions?"

Little Karl's face grew serious for a moment. "Mother, what if there were no poor people? Why can't we all have the things we need?"

Little Karl's mother did not have an answer.

Little Karl spoke again. "Mother, what if we all had clean water and medicine to make us feel better?"
Little Karl's mother did not have an answer.

Little Karl spoke again. "Mother, what if we could all work in peace and happiness?"
Little Karl's mother coughed. She still did not have an answer.

Little Karl kept talking.
"And what if, mother, there were no classes of people? What if everybody had a job? What if we all were happy…"

"...and free," Little Karl finished with a yawn.

Little Karl's mother shook her head gently. "My sweet, silly boy. Only a child could think of such nonsense. And just as children must have things decided for them, so must the lesser of men be ruled by the greater. It's just like your nap. I know better than you, and so nap you must. All children must nap!"

Little Karl rolled over, already dozing off.
"Perhaps, mother. But if the children of the world unite, we shall have nothing to lose but our naps!"

THE END

ABOUT THE AUTHOR

With work for children and adults, M. Earl Smith is a writer who seeks to stretch the boundaries of genre and style. A native of southeast Tennessee, Smith moved to Ohio at nineteen and, with success, reinvented himself as a writer. After graduating from Chatfield College in 2015, Smith enrolled at the University of Pennsylvania in Philadelphia to study creative writing and history. He is the proud father of two wonderful children and, when he's not studying, splits his time between Philadelphia, Cincinnati, and Chattanooga, with road trips to New York City, Wichita, Kansas, and Northampton, Massachusetts.

ABOUT THE ILLUSTRATOR

E. A. Santoli is an illustrator and teacher. He is a graduate of the University of Pennsylvania and the Pennsylvania Academy of the Fine Arts. His inspirations are bridged between academic painting and Japanese manga and anime. He currently resides in Ridgewood, New Jersey.

CPSIA information can be obtained
at www.ICGtesting.com
Printed in the USA
LVOW05s1441270317
528624LV00005B/60/P